APPALACHIAN SPRING

This note appeared in the scores of the original chamber ensemble suite for 13 instruments, and the suite for symphony orchestra:

> *Appalachian Spring* was composed in 1943–44 as a ballet for Miss Martha Graham on a commission from the Elisabeth Sprague Coolidge Foundation. It was first performed by Miss Graham and her company at the Coolidge Festival in the Library of Congress, Washington, D.C., on October 30, 1944.
>
> The action of the ballet concerns "a pioneer celebration in spring around a newly-built farmhouse in the Pennsylvania hills in the early part of the last century [1800s]. The bride-to-be and the young farmer-husband enact the emotions, joyful and apprehensive, their new domestic partnership invites. An Older neighbor suggests now and then the rocky confidence of experience. A revivalist and his followers remind the new householders of the strange and terrible aspects of human fate. At the end the couple is left quiet and strong in their new house."
>
> In 1945 *Appalachian Spring* received the Pulitzer Prize for music, as well as the award of the Music Critics Circle of New York for the outstanding theatrical work of the season of 1944–45.

ABOUT THE VIOLIN AND PIANO TRANSCRIPTION

We have consulted the scores of the original version for 13 instrument chamber ensemble and the composer's 1945 suite for symphony orchestra. For this violin and piano transcription, we have divided the standard orchestral suite into six movements. The movements may be performed consecutively and continuously, without pause, to render the entire music in the standard orchestral suite from the ballet. All tempo indications and expressive markings have been retained, as have most articulations. Adjustments have been made to create an idiomatic work for violin and piano.

Suite from Appalachian Spring

(Ballet for Martha)
in Six Movements

AARON COPLAND
Transcribed for violin and piano
by Bryan Stanley

I

2

a tempo

mp

a tempo

p

4

mp espress.

p

5

p espress.

As at first

p

pp

8vb -

[attacca if continuing
on to II]

II

6 **Allegro** (♩ = 160)

III

[attacca if continuing
on to IV]

IV

28 **More deliberate tempo** (♩ = 126)

Meno mosso 34

Optional ending

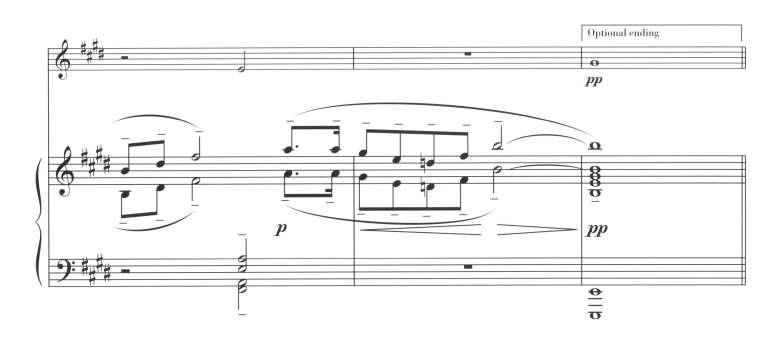

Segue to next movement   **Meno mosso ancora**

[attacca]

V

* In Copland's orchestral and chamber original orchestration, there is a marking to play "at the frog."
Since this effect was originally intended for a violin section, it should likely be omitted by a solo player.

* See note on pg. 21.

* See note on pg. 21.

VI

* Shaker Melody: "The gift to be simple"
  The first bar is only played if this is performed as a stand-alone movement.

62 **Doppio movimento**

Optional ending

67 **Moderato (like a prayer)** (♩ = 66)

Segue to final section

poco rit.

68 **a tempo**
[con sord.]

poco rit.

69 **Più mosso** (♩ = 88–104)

poco rit.

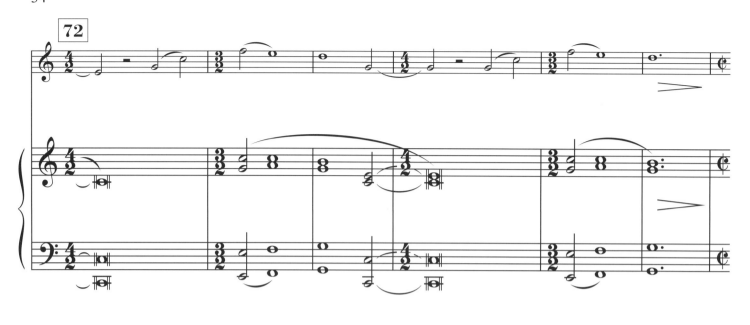

Slower still
("white" tone)

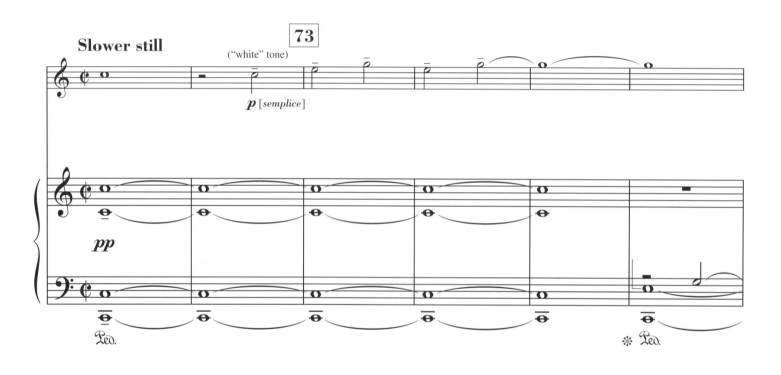

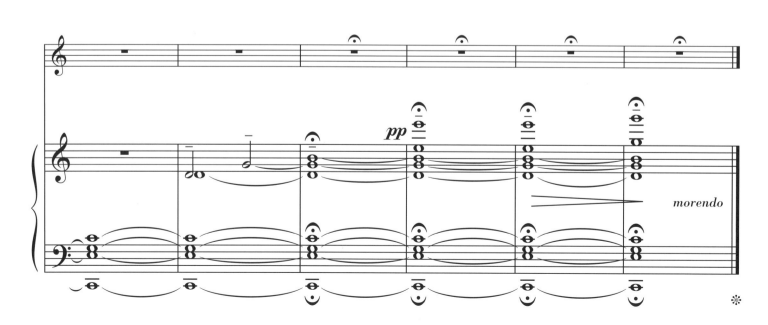